Support for Handwrit

Book 4

Louis Fidge

Illustrated by Chris Hahner

Contents

Name: _____

This sentence contains every letter of the alphabet.
It is written in **unjoined writing**.

A quick brown fox

jumps over the lazy dog.

This is written in **joined writing**.
What differences can you see?

A quick brown fox

jumps over the lazy dog.

Practise the new *f* and *k* shapes.

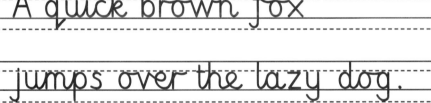

ƒ ƒ ƒ

k k k

Name: _____

There are **four basic joins** in handwriting.
Here is an example of the **first join**.

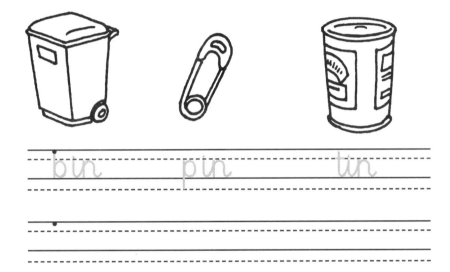

bin   pin   tin

a pin in a tin   a tin in a bin

Name: _____

Match the words and pictures.

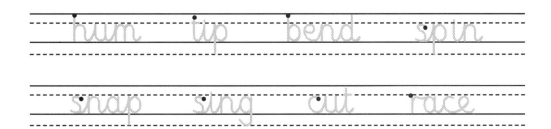

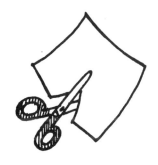   

Name: _____

Copy and write

a ted in a bed   a hen in a pen

a man and a pan   a mug and a jug

a cat in a hat   a pup in a cup

4

Name: _____

Copy and write.

I can see the sun.

I can see the sea.

I can see the sand.

I can hear the band.

Name: _____

Copy and write.

I can saw.

I can skip.

I can hide.

I can mend the car.

I can tie my tie.

I can dig in the mud.

I can tap dance.

Name: _____

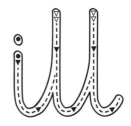

There are **four basic joins** in handwriting.
Here is an example of the **second join**.

Copy and write.

I am climbing the hill.

I am paying the bill.

I am shutting the till.

Name: _____

Copy and write.

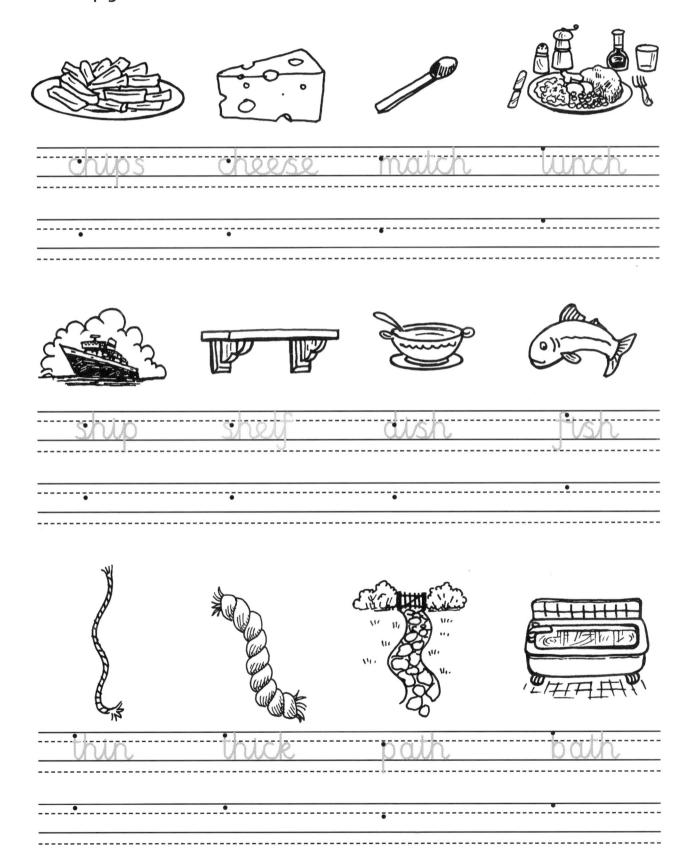

chips   cheese   match   lunch

ship   shelf   dish   fish

thin   thick   path   bath

Name: _____

Copy and write.

I like my bike.   *I like my milkshake.*

I like my skates.   *I like my cake.*

I hate my hat!

Name: _____

Copy and write.

A duck quacks.

A snail has a shell.

A chicken likes to peck.

A lamb is a baby sheep.

Name: _____

Copy and write.

A panther is a big black cat.

A termite is like an ant.

An elephant has a trunk.

A snake hisses and hides.

(11)

Name: _____

There are **four basic joins** in handwriting.
Here is an example of the **third join**.

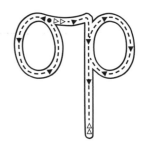

Copy and write.

mop   top   pop in the shop

fog   frog   a dog on a log

Name: _____

Copy and write.

a fox in a box   a sock on a clock

a goat with a coat   a boy with a toy

a toad in the road   a bone under the phone

Name: _____

Copy and write.

The cow moos.

The dove coos.

This mouse is in the house.

This clown wears a crown.

Look at how the kangaroo hops!

Name: _____

Copy and write.

A fire burns brightly.

Some waves are very big.

A rainbow is quite pretty.

The worm wriggles along a wall.

Name: _____

Copy and write.

Four rockets are going to the stars.

Three big trucks are carrying cars.

Two sailing boats are out at sea.

One tired boy in bed – that's me!

Name: _____

Introducing the fourth join

There are **four basic joins** in handwriting.
Here is an example of the **fourth join**.

Copy and write.

old   cold   fold   gold

 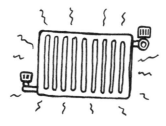  

cot   hot   sob   rob

Name: _____

Copy and write.

a hot pot

a black spot

a dark park

a fierce shark

a mole in a hole

a lovely doll

Name: _____

Copy and write.

A dog likes to bark.   An owl likes to hoot.

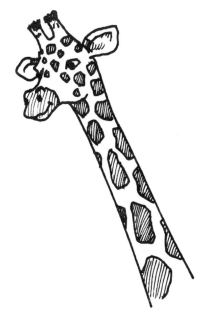

A giraffe has a long neck.

A flamingo has long legs.

19

Name: _____

Copy and write.

The girl has a spotty skirt.

The boy has a dirty shirt.

Butterflies like to flutter by flowers.

20

Name: _____

Copy the sentences.

We use words like who, what, where

and why when we ask questions.

We whisper softly. We whistle loudly.

21

Name: _____

We **never** make **joins** after some letters.
These are called **break letters**.
The break letters are: **b g j p q x y z**

Copy and write.

a queen bee   a jumping gerbil

some young foxes   a stripy zebra

Name: _____

Always begin sentences with a capital letter.
Begin the names of people with capital letters.
Never join up **capital letters**.

Sam

Now write the names of three friends.

----------------------------   ----------------------------   ----------------------------
----------------------------   ----------------------------   ----------------------------

Name _____

(24)

Name _____   ## Pupil's progress sheet

Page	Letters	Date	Comments
1	Introducing joined writing		
2	Introducing the first join		
3	Practising the first join (1)		
4	Practising the first join (2)		
5	Practising the first join (3)		
6	Practising the first join (4)		
7	Introducing the second join		
8	Practising the second join (1)		
9	Practising the second join (2)		
10	Practising the second join (3)		
11	Practising the second join (4)		
12	Introducing the third join		
13	Practising the third join (1)		
14	Practising the third join (2)		
15	Practising the third join (3)		
16	Practising the third join (4)		
17	Introducing the fourth join		
18	Practising the fourth join (1)		
19	Practising the fourth join (2)		
20	Practising the fourth join (3)		
21	Practising the fourth join (4)		
22	Break letters		
23	Capital letters		